Selected from
THE
Mambo
Kings
PLAY
Songs of Love

❋

Oscar Hijuelos

WRITERS' VOICES
New Readers Press

Selection: From *The Mambo Kings Play Songs of Love* by
Oscar Hijuelos. Copyright © 1989 by Oscar Hijuelos.
Reprinted by permission of Farrar, Straus and Giroux, Inc.

New Readers Press
U.S. Publishing Division of Laubach Literacy International
Box 131, Syracuse, New York 13210-0131

Printed in the United States of America
10 9 8 7 6 5 4 3 2

First printing: May 1992
ISBN 0-929631-53-6

The words "Writers Voices" are a trademark of
New Readers Press

Cover designed by Paul Davis Studio
Interior designed by Jules Perlmutter/Off-Broadway Graphics

Acknowledgements

We gratefully acknowledge the generous support of the following foundations and corporations that made the publication of WRITERS' VOICES and NEW WRITERS' VOICES possible: An anonymous foundation; The Vincent Astor Foundation; Exxon Corporation; Knight Foundation; Scripps Howard Foundation; Uris Brothers Foundation and H. W. Wilson Foundation.

This book could not have been realized without the kind and generous cooperation of the author, Oscar Hijuelos, and his publisher, Farrar, Straus and Giroux, Inc. Thanks to Elise Pritchard, Permissions Department.

Our thanks to Paul Davis Studio and Myrna Davis, Paul Davis, Lisa Mazur, Chalkey Calderwood and Alex Ginns for their inspired design of the covers of these books. Thanks also to Jules Perlmutter for his sensitive design of the interior of this book. Thanks also to AnneLouise Burns for map design.

Contents

Note to the Reader

❋

*T*he *Mambo Kings Play Songs of Love* is a bittersweet tale of music, memories and Cuban-Americans. The novel brings to life New York City in the 1950s, with its lively nightclubs where mambo music filled the air with excitement. It features two unforgettable characters, the Castillo brothers.

Every writer has a special voice. That is why we call our series *Writers' Voices*. We chose *The Mambo Kings Play Songs of Love* because the voice of Oscar Hijuelos can be clearly heard as he captures the unique experience of Cuban musicians in New York in the 1950s. We selected portions of *The Mambo Kings Play Songs of Love* that reveal the dreams and disappointments of the Castillo brothers. You'll learn about the rich and colorful world of Latin music. You'll read about Desi Arnaz, the famous Cuban bandleader and star of the *I Love Lucy* show. And you will discover how one moment of glory can affect someone for the rest of his life.

Reading "About the Selections from *The Mambo Kings Play Songs of Love*" will help you begin thinking about what you will read in the selections.

In addition to the selections from *The Mambo Kings Play Songs of Love*, this book includes chapters with interesting or helpful information related to the selections. You may read these before or after reading the selections. You may choose to read some or all of these chapters.

• If you would like more information about Cuban music, including the mambo, look at the chapter called "Latin Music and the Cuban-American Experience" on page 58.

• Many readers enjoy finding out about the person who wrote the book. Sometimes this information will give you more insight into the story. You can find out about Oscar Hijuelos in the chapter that begins on page 56.

If you are a new reader, you may want to have this book read aloud to you, perhaps more than once. Even if you are a more experienced reader, you may enjoy hearing it read aloud before reading it silently to yourself.

We encourage you to read *actively*. Here are some things you can do.

Before Reading

- Read the front and back covers of the book, and look at the cover illustration. Ask yourself what you expect the book to be about.

- Think about why you want to read this book. Are you interested in music or dancing? Are you from Cuba or another island in the Caribbean? Did you enjoy the *I Love Lucy* show?

- Look at the Contents page. See where you can find a glossary of Spanish words, a chronology of events in the novel, a map and other information. Decide what you want to read and in what order.

During Reading

- There may be Spanish words, names of characters and slang words that are difficult to read. Keep reading to see if the meaning becomes clear. If it doesn't, go back and re-read the difficult part or discuss it with others. You can also look at the Spanish-English glossary on page 50, which lists many of the difficult words.

- Ask yourself questions as you read. For example: What are the differences between the two brothers? How are they alike? What kind of person is Desi Arnaz, as portrayed in this book?

After Reading

- Think about what you have read. Did you identify with either of the brothers? How would you feel if you were asked to be on a popular television show like *I Love Lucy*? Did the book make you see any of your own experiences in a new light?
- Talk with others about your thoughts.
- Try some of the questions and activities in "Questions for the Reader" on page 52. They are meant to help you discover more about what you have read and how it relates to you.

The editors of *Writers' Voices* hope you will write to us. We want to know your thoughts about our books.

About the Selections from
The
MAMBO KINGS
Play
SONGS OF LOVE

Oscar Hijuelos's *The Mambo Kings Play Songs of Love* was published in 1989. Most of the story takes place in New York City in the 1950s. It is about two brothers, Cesar and Nestor Castillo. They are from the island-nation of Cuba.

In 1949, the brothers come to New York from Cuba to make their way as musicians. They form a band called the Mambo Kings. The mambo is a type of music and dance that began in Cuba and became very popular in the United States during the 1950s. You can learn more about the mambo in the chapter "Latin Music and the Cuban-American Experience."

The brothers have very different personalities. Cesar is the more outgoing of the two. He has left his wife and daughter in Cuba to come to America. Cesar loves the night life and chasing women.

Nestor, on the other hand, is shy and somber. As a young man in Cuba he had a brief love affair with a woman named María. She is the inspiration for the song Nestor writes and both brothers play, "Beautiful María of My Soul."

The brothers become fairly successful musicians. Their Mambo Kings band plays in glamorous nightclubs in New York and around the country. The highlight comes in 1955. Desi Arnaz, the most famous Cuban bandleader of the time, and his wife, Lucille Ball, visit a club where the brothers are playing. He asks them to make a guest appearance on his hit television show, *I Love Lucy*.

Most of the novel is told by Nestor's son, Eugenio. In the first part of the selections, Eugenio remembers seeing, as a child, a rerun of his father and uncle on the *I Love Lucy* show. By this time, however, Nestor has died and Eugenio's Uncle Cesar's career has gone downhill. He plays at night in local social clubs. By day, he works as a building super-intendent.

The Mambo Kings Play Songs of Love describes a world in which music and dance provided an escape from the sometimes harsh realities of immigrant life. Another source of strength was the close local community of Cuban-Americans. No matter where they lived in America, when Cuban-Americans met, they recognized their common roots.

Perhaps the selections will remind you of your own cultural roots. Or you might think about how a very special event could affect the rest of a person's life.

Selected from
THE
Mambo Kings
PLAY
Songs of Love

Oscar Hijuelos

❅

1 Eugenio Early 1960s

It was a Saturday afternoon [in New York City], years and years ago when I was a little kid, and around three o'clock Mrs. Shannon, the heavy Irish woman in her perpetually soup-stained dress, opened her back window and shouted out into the courtyard, "Hey, Cesar, yoo-hoo, I think you're on television, I swear it's you!" When I heard the opening strains of the *I Love Lucy* show I got excited because I knew she was referring to an item of eternity, that episode in which my dead father and my Uncle Cesar had appeared, playing Ricky Ricardo's singing cousins fresh off the farm in Oriente Province, Cuba, and north in New York for an engagement at Ricky's nightclub, the Tropicana.

This was close enough to the truth about their real lives—they were musicians and songwriters who had left Havana for New York in 1949, the year they formed the Mambo Kings, an orchestra that packed clubs, dance halls, and theaters around the East Coast—and, excitement of excitements, they even made a fabled journey in a flamingo-pink bus out to Sweet's Ballroom in San Francisco, playing on an all-star mambo night, a beautiful night of glory, beyond death, beyond pain, beyond all stillness.

Desi Arnaz had caught their act one night in a supper club on the West Side, and because they had perhaps already known each other from Havana or Oriente Province, where Arnaz, like the brothers, was born, it was natural that he ask them to sing on his show. He liked one of their songs in particular, a romantic bolero written by them, "Beautiful María of My Soul."

Some months later (I don't know how many, I wasn't five years old yet) they began to rehearse for the immortal appearance of my father on this show. For me, my father's gentle rapping on Ricky Ricardo's door has always been a call from the beyond, as in Dracula films, or films of the walking dead, in which spirits ooze out from behind tombstones and through the cracked windows and rotted floors of gloomy antique halls: Lucille Ball, the lovely redheaded actress and comedienne who played Ricky's wife, was housecleaning when she heard the rapping of my father's knuckles against that door.

"I'm commmmmming," in her singsong voice.

Standing in her entrance, two men in white silk suits and butterfly-looking lace bow ties, black instrument cases by their side and black-brimmed white hats in their hands—my father, Nestor Castillo, thin and broad-shouldered, and Uncle Cesar, thickset and immense.

My uncle: "Mrs. Ricardo? My name is Alfonso and this is my brother Manny..."

And her face lights up and she says, "Oh, yes, the fellows from Cuba. Ricky told me all about you."

Then, just like that, they're sitting on the couch when Ricky Ricardo walks in and says something like, "Manny, Alfonso! Gee, it's really swell that you fellas could make it up here from Havana for the show."

That's when my father smiled. The first time I saw a rerun of this, I could remember other things about him—his lifting me up, his smell of cologne, his patting my head, his handing me a dime, his touching my face, his whistling, his taking me and my little sister, Leticia, for a walk in the park, and so many other moments happening in my thoughts simultaneously that it was like watching something momentous, say the Resurrection, as if Christ had stepped out of his sepulcher, flooding the world with light—what we were taught in the local church with the big red doors—because my father was now newly alive and could take off his hat and sit down on the couch in Ricky's living room, resting his black instrument case on his lap. He could play the trumpet, move his head, blink his eyes, nod, walk across the room, and say "Thank you" when offered a cup of coffee. For me, the room was suddenly bursting with a silvery radiance. And now I knew that we could see it again. Mrs. Shannon had called out into the courtyard alerting my uncle: I was already in his apartment.

With my heart racing, I turned on the big black-and-white television set in his living room and tried to wake him. My uncle had fallen asleep in the kitchen—having worked really late the night before, some job in a Bronx social club, singing and playing the horn with a pickup group of musicians. He was snoring, his shirt was open, a few buttons had popped out on his belly. Between the delicate-looking index and forefingers of his right hand, a Chesterfield cigarette burning down to the filter, that hand still holding a half glass of rye whiskey, which he used to drink like crazy because in recent years he had been suffering from bad dreams, saw apparitions, felt cursed, and, despite all the women he took to bed, found his life of bachelorhood solitary and wearisome. But I didn't know this at the time, I thought he was sleeping because he had worked so hard the night before, singing and playing the trumpet for seven or eight hours. I'm talking about a wedding party in a crowded, smoke-filled room (with bolted-shut fire doors), lasting from nine at night to four, five o'clock in the morning, the band playing one-, two-hour sets. I thought he just needed the rest. How could I have known that he

would come home and, in the name of un-
winding, throw back a glass of rye, then a
second, and then a third, and so on, until he'd
plant his elbow on the table and use it to steady
his chin, as he couldn't hold his head up oth-
erwise. But that day I ran into the kitchen to
wake him up so that he could see the episode,
too, shaking him gently and tugging at his
elbow, which was a mistake, because it was
as if I had pulled loose the support columns
of a five-hundred-year-old church: he simply
fell over and crashed to the floor.

A commercial was running on the television, and so, as I knew I wouldn't have much
time, I began to slap his face, pull on his burning red-hot ears, tugging on them until he finally opened one eye. In the act of focusing
he apparently did not recognize me, because
he asked, "Nestor, what are you doing here?"

"It's me, Uncle, it's Eugenio."

He said, "You?"

"Yes, Uncle, get up! Please get up! You're
on television again. Come on."

One thing I have to say about my Uncle
Cesar, there was very little he wouldn't do for
me in those days, and so he nodded, tried to
push himself off the floor, got to his knees,
had trouble balancing, and then fell back-

wards. His head must have hurt: his face was a wince of pain. Then he seemed to be sleeping again. From the living room came the voice of Ricky's wife, plotting as usual with her ~neighbor Ethel Mertz about how to get a part on Ricky's show at the Tropicana, and I knew that the brothers had already been to the apartment—that's when Mrs. Shannon had called out into the courtyard—that in about five more minutes my father and uncle would be standing on the stage of the Tropicana, ready to perform that song again. Ricky would take hold of the microphone and say, "Well, folks, and now I have a real treat for you. Ladies and gentlemen, Alfonso and Manny Reyes, let's hear it!" And soon my father and uncle would be standing side by side, living, breathing beings, for all the world to see, harmonizing in a duet of that *canción*.

As I shook my uncle, he opened his eyes and gave me his hand, hard and callused from his other job in those days, as superintendent, and he said, "Eugenio, help me. Help me."

I tugged with all my strength, but it was hopeless. Still he tried: with great effort he made it to one knee, and then, with his hand braced on the floor, he started to push himself up again. As I gave him another tug, he began miraculously to rise. Then he pushed my hand away and said, "I'll be okay, kid."

With one hand on the table and the other on the steam pipe, he pulled himself to his feet.

"*Bueno*," he said.

He followed me into the living room, and plopped down on the couch behind me. I sat on a big stuffed chair that we'd hauled up out of the basement. He squinted at the screen, watching himself and his younger brother, whom, despite their troubles, he loved very much. He seemed to be dreaming.

"Well, folks," Ricky Ricardo said, "and now I have a real treat for you . . ."

The two musicians in white silk suits and big butterfly-looking lace bow ties, marching toward the microphone, my uncle holding a guitar, my father a trumpet.

"Thank you, thank you. And now a little number that we composed . . ." And as Cesar started to strum the guitar and my father lifted his trumpet to his lips, playing the opening of "Beautiful María of My Soul," a lovely, soaring melody line filling the room.

They were singing the song as it had been written—in Spanish. With the Ricky Ricardo Orchestra behind them, they came into a turn-around and began harmonizing a line that translates roughly into English as "What delicious pain love has brought to me in the form of a woman."

My father . . . He looked so alive!

"Uncle!"

Uncle Cesar had lit a cigarette and fallen asleep. His cigarette had slid out of his fingers and was now burning into the starched cuff of his white shirt. I put the cigarette out, and then my uncle, opening his eyes again, smiled. "Eugenio, do me a favor. Get me a drink."

"But, Uncle, don't you want to watch the show?"

He tried really hard to pay attention, to focus on it.

"Look, it's you and Poppy."

"*Coño, sí . . .*"

My father's face with his horsey grin, arching eyebrows, big fleshy ears—a family trait— that slight look of pain, his quivering vocal cords, how beautiful it all seemed to me then . . .

And so I rushed into the kitchen and came back with a glass of rye whiskey, charging as fast as I could without spilling it. Ricky had joined the brothers onstage. He was definitely pleased with their performance and showed it because as the last note sounded he whipped up his hand and shouted "*Olé*," a big lock of his thick black hair falling over his brows. Then they bowed and the audience applauded.

The show continued on its course. A few gags followed: a costumed bull with flowers wrapped around its horns came out dancing an Irish jig, its horn poking into Ricky's bottom and so exasperating him that his eyes bugged out, he slapped his forehead and started speaking a-thousand-words-a-second Spanish. But at that point it made no difference to me, the miracle had passed, the resurrection of a man, Our Lord's promise which I then believed, with its release from pain, release from the troubles of this world.

2 How it was 1955

One Tuesday night in 1955 the Cuban band-leader and television personality Desi Arnaz walked into the Mambo Nine Club on 58th Street and Eighth Avenue to check out the talent. Someone had told him about two Cuban brothers, Cesar and Nestor Castillo, that they were good singers and songwriters who might have some material for Arnaz to use on his show. The stage of the Mambo Nine was only ten feet wide, more suited for a cabaret act than for a thirteen-piece orchestra, but somehow the brothers' group, the Mambo Kings, set up with their congas, their horns, trombones, flute, stand-up bass, saxophones, and a grand piano behind a few ball microphones. It was a place where musicians from the best bands in the city came in to drink, talk shop, and see what was going on. Under the glow of red-and-white stage lights the Mambo Kings played fast dance tunes like "*El Bodeguero*" and dreamy arrangements of slow, romantic boleros like "*Bésame Mucho.*" Mr. Arnaz was sitting in the back with his pretty wife, the red glow of a candle vaguely illuminating his dark, intense eyes, liking very much what he was seeing and hearing . . . In white silk suits, and performing side by side before the big ball microphone, the two brothers showed an obvious affection for each other, the audience, and the music. Arnaz, chin resting on a fist, came to certain conclusions about them.

Cesar began to sing the verses Nestor had been writing on a cold, lonely night spent shivering by a radiator, verses inspired by the Havana beauty who had broken his heart.

Among those lyrics, these lines:

> ... How can I hate you
> if I love you so?
> I can't explain my torment,
> for I don't know how to live
> without your love ...
> What delicious pain
> love has brought to me
> in the form of a woman.
> My torment and ecstasy,
> María, my life,
> Beautiful María of my soul ...

Arnaz listened attentively. During the chorus, when the two brothers were harmonizing like angels aloft on a cloud and confiding their pain, Arnaz thought about his own past love, his love for his wife and others, like his family down in Cuba and old friends he had not seen in a long time. As he watched the dance floor, where young couples sighed and kissed, Arnaz leaned over to his wife and said, "I must invite these fellows to play on the show."

Later, when the brothers were drinking by the bar, Arnaz lived up to his reputation as a friendly man and introduced himself, saying, with extended hand, "Desi Arnaz." He was wearing a sharp blue serge suit, white silk shirt, pink polka-dotted tie, and a frilly fringed handkerchief that bloomed like a tulip from his breast pocket. He shook their hands and ordered a round of drinks for all the musicians, complimented the brothers on their performance, and then invited them to sit at his table. Then they met Lucille Ball, who spoke surprisingly good Spanish. She was dressed in a pearl-button blouse with a velvet diamond-broached vest and a long skirt. Her hands and wrists glittered with rings and bracelets and she had curly red hair that had been done up in a bouffant, and beautiful blue eyes.

As this was a time when every Cuban in New York knew every other Cuban, the question was inevitable: "And what part of Cuba are you fellows from?"

"From a town called Las Piñas, surely you must know it, a sugar-mill town in Oriente."

"Of course, I come from Santiago de Cuba myself. I'm from Oriente, too!"

The knowledge that they were all from the same part of the world made them shake hands and nod at Arnaz in a brotherly way, as if they'd known each other for years and years.

"We grew up on the sugar mill and then

we moved over to a farm when our father tried the livestock business," Cesar told Arnaz. "But I had to get out of there and bring my brother here with me. Cutting off the heads of animals wasn't for us . . . Besides, I'd always wanted to be a singer, *tú sabes*, since my childhood, I always did my best to hang around musicians."

"It was the exact same thing for me," Arnaz said.

At that point the other Mambo Kings, black instrument cases in hand, came over to say goodbye for the night and to thank Mr. Arnaz again for the drinks. They were all crowded around the table, laughing and nodding, as Arnaz joked with them in Spanish and complimented them on their playing. It was then that Cesar leaned over to his younger brother, consulted for a moment, and then, after the others had left, said to Arnaz, "We're going to have a late-night dinner at our apartment on La Salle Street uptown. May I invite you and your wife to join us? My brother's wife always cooks up a feast and tonight we're having *arroz con pollo*, black beans, and *plátanos*."

"Yes?"

And Arnaz consulted with his wife. They

heard her saying, "But, sweetheart, we have some business in the morning."

"I know, I know, but I'm hungry, and who feels like going to a restaurant now?"

So he turned and told the brothers, "Why not?" and soon they were out in the street in their long coats and brimmed hats, blowing into their cupped hands and stomping their feet on the sidewalk. While they had been inside, it had started snowing, and now it was still coming down, a heaven of snow falling in all directions on every street and building, awning, car, and tree. Cesar was out on the avenue calling a yellow cab, and shortly they were all huddled together in the back. Nestor and Cesar sat on the small metal flip-up seats, facing the rear window and their new friends.

The building on La Salle Street was nothing like what Arnaz and his wife were accustomed to: they had houses in Connecticut and California, and an apartment in Havana. And it was nothing like what the brothers had known in Cuba, a modest house made of pine timbers facing a field ringed by fruit trees and rhapsodic with birdsong in the late-afternoon sun, a sky bursting with bands of red, yellow, pink,

and silver light and burning treetops, and or-
ange-tinged black birds. No, it was a six-story
building, the kind one would never dream
about living in for the rest of one's life, situated
near the top of a hill, with an ordinary stoop,
basement stairs, and narrow, dim-lit entrance.

Opening the front door, Nestor felt a little
nervous and self-conscious; he had been that
way since the day of their arrival in the States,
six years before.

As they climbed the stairs up to the fourth
floor, where Cesar and Nestor and his family
lived, Arnaz began to whistle the melody of
the song he'd heard earlier that night, "Beautiful María of My Soul."

When his nostrils hit the good food smells
in the hallway of the apartment, Arnaz slapped
his hands together and declared, ''¡Qué bueno!
How wonderful!'' He found himself moving
along a hallway whose walls were covered
with framed photographs of musicians and
portraits of Jesus Christ and his saints.

"Make yourself at home, *compañero*," Cesar
said in his normal friendly manner. "Now this
is your home, you understand, Mr. Arnaz?"

"Sounds good to me. Now, Lucy, isn't this
nice?"

"Yes, it is, Desi, just swell."

"Ah, do I smell some *plátanos*?"

"*Plátanos verdes,*" a female voice called from the kitchen.

"And *yuca* with *ajo*?"

"Yes," said Cesar happily. "And we have wine, we have beer!" He raised up his hands. "We have rum!"

"*¡Qué bueno!*"

It was around one in the morning and Delores Castillo was in the kitchen, heating up all the pots of rice and chicken and beans, and the fritters were sizzling in a frying pan. Her hair was in a bun and she had a stained apron around her waist. When they all jammed into the kitchen, Delores recognized the famous Arnaz and his wife.

"*Dios mío!*" she cried. "If I had known they were coming, I would have cleaned the house up."

Regaining her composure, Delores smiled so beautifully that Arnaz told her, "Mrs. Castillo, you're a lovely woman." The coats were left in the bedroom, and soon enough they were all gathered around the kitchen table. While the men devoured the food, Delores hurried down the hall and woke her children up. Eugenio's eyes were barely open when he felt himself being carried down the hall, his mother saying to him, "I want you to meet someone." She put him down the kitchen doorway and when he looked up he saw the usual scene for that household: a crowded kitchen, mouths chewing, beer and rum bottles open on the table. Even the nice fellow his mother was all excited about looked just like so many of the other musicians who passed through the house. And the name Desi Arnaz meant nothing to him then, it was just a name he heard when she introduced him.

"Mr. Arnaz, this is our boy, Eugenio. And this is Leticia."

Desi Arnaz reached over and pinched his cheek, and he patted Leticia's head. Then they were taken back into their bedrooms, the kids falling asleep to a background of Spanish-speaking voices in the kitchen, the music from the phonograph in the living room, the sound of laughter and clapping, just like what they'd heard on so many other nights.

Cesar walked in with his orange-wood Brazilian guitar and handed it to Arnaz. "Would you sing us a little song, Mr. Arnaz?"

"Why not"—and he placed the guitar on his lap and strummed the C-minor chord, flailing his hand quickly over the strings so that its soundbox vibrated like the wind hitting a shutter, and began to sing one of his biggest hits, *"Babalú."*

"Oh, great Babbbbbbaaaallllooo, oh, why did you forsake me?"

Cesar banged on the table, and Nestor, giving in to the rush of fun, started to play the flute... Then Arnaz began playing *"Cielito Lindo"* and by then everyone in the kitchen was a ring of arms and swaying, happy bodies.

Strummed like a waltz, *"Cielito Lindo"* was the kind of song that a loving mother would sing at bedtime to her children, and that was why the two Mambo Kings remembered wonderful things about their mother, and why Arnaz shut his eyes in pleasant contemplation of his own loving mother in Cuba.

But then around three o'clock Lucille Ball tapped her watch and said to Arnaz, "Now, honey, we have to go."

"Yes, of course. Tomorrow it's work, always work. I'm sorry we have to go, but I want to tell you something before we do. That *canción* you fellows sang at the club tonight, 'Beautiful María,' I really like it and think that you should come on my show and do it for me there."

"Nightclub show?"

"No, I mean my television show."

"Yes!" said Cesar. "Of course, you let us know what we have to do. I'll give you our address." And he rushed off into the hall, looking for a pen and a piece of paper. Later, Cesar was out on Broadway trying to flag down a taxicab for Arnaz and his wife, who were waiting on the curb. They were out there for about twenty minutes before they caught a taxi, its heavy, snow-chained wheels edging their way up the snowy streets.

Arnaz shook Cesar Castillo's hand. "I'm glad we had this chance to meet, my friend. You'll be hearing from me soon enough. Okay? So, *cuídate*, take care of yourself."

Then Arnaz and his wife got into the taxi and disappeared into the night.

California

Desi Arnaz kept his promise and three months later the brothers were on a plane to Hollywood, California. Cesar really loved the trip, loved flying in those big four-engine airplanes and watching the clouds burn up with sunlight. But Nestor? He couldn't believe that all that metal stayed up in the air. The long eleven-hour non-stop flight frightened him.

Desilu Productions put them up in the Garden of Allah Hotel, with a swimming pool, prickly palm trees, and young starlets stretch-

ing out in the sun. Each time they would head
out from the hotel for rehearsals, Nestor would
belt down a glass of whiskey, sometimes two.
He had gotten that way, playing in the big
dance halls. The television studio was over on
Selma Avenue and was so busy that no one
noticed when Nestor would show up a little
drunk. The actual filming of the program was
to take place on a Friday and the players and
musicians would have three days to rehearse.
Everyone involved with the show was nice to
the brothers. Desi Arnaz was especially kind
and generous to the Cubans he'd hired. Ask
anyone about Arnaz in those days and they'd
talk about his friendliness and concern for the
people working for him, like a responsible *pa-
trón*. After all, the man was Cuban and knew
how to present the proper image of a man.

The evening they actually filmed the show
before an audience, Nestor could barely move,
he wanted out so badly. He spent the afternoon pacing back and forth in their hotel
room, a sweaty nervous mess. And at the studio itself he remained in the wings, leaning up
against a Coke machine, watching the bustle
of electricians, sound and light technicians,
cameramen, and script girls all around him,
as if life were passing him by. Something about

singing that song, María's song, before millions, frightened him. His fear frustrated Cesar, who kept saying, *"Tranquilo, tranquilo, hombre.* And just don't forget, we'll have Arnaz out there with us."

Then, as he always did with his younger brother before any performance, Cesar looked him over, brushed the lint off his jacket, pulled down on its hem to make sure his shoulders were straight, and patted Nestor's back. With that the orchestra started to play the *I Love Lucy* theme and someone gave them their cue, and together, guitar and trumpet in hand, they went on.

It was 1955 and Lucille Ball was cleaning in her living room when she heard a knock on the door to her Manhattan apartment, someone gently rapping.

"I'm commmmmming," she answered, touching her hairdo on her way to the door.

Standing there, two men in white silk suits and butterfly-shaped lace bow ties, black instrument cases, guitar and trumpet, by their sides, with black-brimmed cane hats in hand which they'd taken off as she opened the door. The two men nodded and smiled, but there seemed something sad about their expressions, at least in retrospect, as if they knew what would happen to them. The taller and broader of the two, who wore a slick, pimpy-looking mustache, in vogue at the time, cleared his throat and said in a quiet voice, "Mrs. Ricardo? My name is Alfonso and this is my brother Manny..."

"Oh, yes, the fellows from Cuba. Ricky told me all about you. Come on in and make yourselves at home. Ricky'll be out in a minute."

With tremendous politeness the brothers bowed and then sat down on the sofa, each leaning forward, not allowing himself to sink completely into its plump cushions.

Suddenly in walked Ricky Ricardo, night-club singer and musical impresario—the character whom Desi Arnaz played on his television show. He was a pleasant-looking man with large friendly eyes and a thick head of black hair, shiny as sealskin. Dressed in cuffed trousers, wide-lapeled sports jacket, short-collared shirt, and a slick-looking black tie decorated with piano keys and a crocodile-shaped tie clip, he definitely seemed prosperous and self-confident. He walked in with his right hand in his jacket pocket and, when he saw the brothers, rapped each on his back and said, "Manny, Alfonso! Gee, I'm glad to see you! How are things down in Cuba?"

"Fine, Ricky."

"Well, sit down and tell me, did you fellows decide which song you're going to do on my show at the Tropicana?"

"Yes," said the older brother. "We've decided to sing 'Beautiful María of My Soul.'"

"That's swell, fellows. Say, Lucy, wait until you hear the number they're going to do with me for the finale on the show next week. 'Beautiful María of My Soul.'"

The redhead's expression changed, fell to pieces, as if someone had died.

"But Ricky, you promised *me* the chance to sing on the show!"

"Well, I can't discuss it with you now, Lucy. I've got to take the fellows over to the club."

"Please, Ricky, if you let me, I'll never never never ask you again. Please?"

She stood in front of him and looked at him so sweetly and fluttered her eyelashes so endearingly that he began to reconsider. "We'll see, Lucy."

And shaking his head, he started speaking rapidly in Spanish to the brothers: "If you knew what I have to go through every day with this woman. These American women are enough to drive you nuts! My mother told me a million times: Ricky, never marry an American woman unless you're looking for one big headache. And she was right, I should've married that girl back in Cuba! Now there was a quiet girl who never bothered me, who knew where her bread was buttered. She wasn't crazy! She always left me alone, you know what I mean, *compañeros*?"

And in English again, "Let's go."

The brothers put their hats on, took up their instrument cases, and followed the nightclub singer out. When he opened the door, his neighbors, a stout-looking bald man and his wife, a pretty, somewhat matronly blonde, stood before him, flattop straw hats in hand. The two brothers nodded to them and made their way out into the apartment-building hallway and left for the club.

Later, an immense satin heart dissolved and through a haze appeared the interior of the Tropicana nightclub.

At center stage, a large ball microphone, spotlight, drumroll, and Ricky Ricardo.

"Well, folks, tonight I have a special treat for you. Ladies and gentlemen, I am pleased to present to you, direct from Havana, Cuba, Manny and Alfonso Reyes singing a bolero of their own composition, 'Beautiful María of My Soul.'"

The brothers walked out in white suits and with a guitar and trumpet, bowed to the audience, and nodded when Ricky Ricardo faced the orchestra and, holding his conductor's wand, prepared to begin, asked them, "Are you ready?"

The older brother strummed an A-minor chord, the key of the song; a harp swirled in as if from the clouds of heaven; then the bassist began to play a habanera, and then the piano and horns played a four-chord vamp. Standing side by side before the microphone, brows creased in concentration, expressions sincere, the brothers began to sing that romantic bolero "Beautiful María of My Soul." A song about love so far away it hurts; a song about lost pleasures, a song about youth, a song about love so elusive a man can never know where he stands; a song about wanting a woman so much death does not frighten you, a song about wanting that woman even when she has abandoned you.

As Cesar sang, his vocal cords trembling, he seemed to be watching something profoundly beautiful and painful happening in the distance, eyes passionate, imploring, his earnest expression asking, "Can you see who I am?" But the younger brother's eyes were closed and his head was tilted back. He looked like a man on the verge of falling through an eternal abyss of longing and solitude.

For the final verses they were joined by the bandleader, who harmonized with them and was so happy with the song that at the end he whipped his right hand up into the air, a lock of thick black hair falling over his brow. Then he shouted, *"Olé!"* The brothers were now both smiling and taking bows, and Arnaz, playing Ricky Ricardo, said, "Let's give them a nice hand, folks!" The brothers bowed again and shook Arnaz's hand and walked offstage, waving to the audience.

Back in New York

In the days after the broadcast of the show, they became celebrities on La Salle Street: gaunt, ruddy-cheeked Irishmen would step out of the shadows of the Shamrock Bar on the corner and into the late-afternoon light and say to the brothers, "Can I stand you to a glass of beer?" People would stick their heads out of the window to shout hello, passersby stopped them on the street and wished them well. Gossiping old ladies who sat in front of the stoop on frail, thin-legged chairs whispered about the fame that had abruptly descended upon those two "Spanish fellows" who lived in 500; for weeks after, the two brothers had regular fans among the Irish and Germans on the block, and even those people who hadn't seen the show knew about it and treated the musicians with a new respect.

It is now 1981, 26 years after the Castillo brothers appeared on the I Love Lucy *show. That moment was the high point of their careers. Nestor died in a car crash in 1957, two years after their appearance. He was only 31 years old. Cesar struggled to keep playing his music but the times changed. He drank heavily to avoid reality. He finally died in 1980 from alcoholism. Nestor's son, Eugenio, has traveled to California to meet Desi Arnaz.*

3 *Eugenio 1981*

When I called the number that had been listed on Desi Arnaz's letterhead, I expected to speak with a secretary, but it was Mr. Arnaz himself who answered the phone.

"Mr. Arnaz?"

"Yes."

"I'm Eugenio Castillo."

"Ah, Eugenio Castillo, Nestor's son?"

"Yes."

"Nice to hear from you, and where are you calling from?"

"From Los Angeles."

"Los Angeles? What brings you out here?"

"Just a vacation."

"Well then, if you are so close by, you must come to visit me."

"Yes?"

"Of course. Can you come out tomorrow?"

"Yes."

"Then come. In the late afternoon. I'll be waiting to see you."

It had taken me a long time to finally work up the nerve to call Desi Arnaz. About a year ago, when I had written to him about my uncle, he was kind enough to send his condolences and ended that letter with an invitation to his home. When I finally decided to take him up on his offer and flew to Los Angeles, where I stayed in a motel near the airport, I had wanted to call him every day for two weeks. But I was afraid that his kindness would turn into air, like so many other things in this life, or that he would be dif-

ferent from what I had imagined. Or he
would be cruel or disinterested, or simply not
really concerned about visitors like me. Instead, I drank beer by the motel swimming
pool and passed my days watching jet planes
crossing the sky. Then I made the acquain-
tance of one of the blondes by the pool, and
she seemed to have a soft spot for guys like
me, and we fell desperately in love for a
week. Then ended things badly. But one
afternoon, [I picked up the phone]. Once I'd
arranged the visit, my next problem was to
get out to Belmont. On the map, it was about
thirty miles north of San Diego along the
coast, but I didn't drive. So I ended up on a
bus that got me into Belmont around three
in the afternoon. Then I took a cab and soon
found myself standing before the entranceway to Desi Arnaz's estate.

A stone wall covered with bougainvillea,
like the flower-covered walls of Cuba, and
flowers everywhere. Inside the gate, a walk-
way to the large pink ranch-style house with
a tin roof, a garden, a patio, and a swimming
pool. Arched doorways and shuttered windows. Iron balconies on the second floor. And
there was a front garden where hibiscus, chry-
santhemums, and roses grew. Somehow I had
expected to hear the *I Love Lucy* theme, but

that place, outside of birdsong, the rustling of trees, and the sound of water running in a fountain, was utterly tranquil. Birds chirping everywhere, and a gardener in blue coveralls standing in the entranceway of the house, looking over the mail spread out on a table. He was a white-haired, slightly stooped man, thick around the middle, with a jowly face, a bundle of letters in one hand, a cigar in the other.

As I approached him, saying, "Hello?" he turned around, extended his hand, and said, "Desi Arnaz."

When I shook his hand, I could feel his callused palms. His hands were mottled with age spots, his fingers nicotine-stained, and the face that had charmed millions looked much older, but when he smiled, the young Arnaz's face revealed itself.

Immediately, he said, "Ah, but you must be hungry. Would you like a sandwich? Or a steak?" Then: "Come with me."

I followed Desi Arnaz down his hallway.

"I'm retired these days," Mr. Arnaz said, leading me through the house. "Sometimes I'll do a little television show, like Merv Griffin, but I mainly like to spend my time with my children or in my garden."

When we had passed out of the house

through another arched doorway, we reached a patio that looked out over Arnaz's trees and terraced gardens. There were pear, apricot, and orange trees everywhere, a pond in which floated water lilies. Pinks and yellows and brilliant reds coming out of the ground and clustered in bushes. And beyond all this, the Pacific Ocean.

". . . But I can't complain. I love my flowers and little plants."

He rang a bell and a Mexican woman came out of the house.

"Make some sandwiches and bring us some beer. Dos Equis, huh?"

Bowing, the maid backed out through a doorway.

"So, what can I do for you, my boy? What is it that you have there?"

"I brought something for you."

They were just some of my uncle's and father's records from back when, Mambo King recordings. There were five of them, just some old 78s and a 33, "The Mambo Kings Play Songs of Love." Looking over the first of the records, he sucked in air through his teeth fiercely. On the cover of that record my father and uncle were posed together, playing a drum and blowing a trumpet for a pretty woman in a tight dress. Putting that aside, and nodding, he looked at the others.

"Your father and uncle. They were good fellows." And: "Good songwriters."

And he started to sing "Beautiful María of My Soul," and although he couldn't remember all the words, he filled in the missing phrases with humming.

"A good song filled with emotion and affection."

Then he looked over the others. "Are you selling these?"

"No, because I want to give them to you."

"Why, thank you, my boy."

The maid brought in our sandwiches, nice thick roast beef, lettuce, and tomato, and mustard, on rye bread, and the beers. We ate quietly. Every now and then, Arnaz would look up at me through heavy-lidded eyes and smile.

"You know, *hombre*," Arnaz said, chewing. "I wish there was something I could do for you." Then: "The saddest thing in life is when someone dies, don't you think, *chico*?"

"What did you say?"

"I said, do you like California?"

"Yes."

"It's beautiful. I chose this climate here because it reminds me of Cuba. Here grow many

of the same plants and flowers. You know, me
and your father and uncle came from the same
province, Oriente. I haven't been back there
in over twenty years. Could you have imagined what Fidel would have made of Desi Arnaz going back to Cuba? Have you ever been
there?"

"No."

"Well, that's a shame. It's a little like this."
He stretched and yawned.

"Tell you what we'll do, boy. We'll set you
up in the guest room, and then I'll show you
around. Do you ride horses?"

"No."

"A shame." He winced, straightening up his
back. "Do me a favor, boy, and give me a hand
up."

Arnaz reached out and I pulled him to his
feet.

"Come on, I'll show you my different gardens."

Beyond the patio, down a few steps, was
another stairway, and that led to another patio, bounded by a wall. A thick scent of flowers
in the air.

"This garden is modeled after one of my
favorite little plazas in Santiago. You came
across it on your way to the harbor. I used to

take my girls there." And he winked. "Those days are long gone.

"And from this *placita* you could see all of Santiago Bay. At sunset the sky burned red, and that's when, if you were lucky, you might steal a kiss. Or make like Cuban Pete. That's one of the songs that made me famous."

Nostalgically, Arnaz sang, "My name is Cuban Pete, I'm the King of the Rumba Beat!"

Then we both stood for a moment looking at how the Pacific seemed to go on forever and forever.

"One day, all this will either be gone or it will last forever. Which do you think?"

"About what?"

"The afterlife. I believe in it. You?"

I shrugged.

"Maybe there's nothing. But I can remember when life felt like it would last forever. You're a young man, you wouldn't understand. You know what was beautiful, boy? When I was little and my mother would hold me in her arms."

I wanted to fall on my knees and beg him to save me. I wanted to hold him tight and hear him say, "I love you," just so I could show Arnaz that I really did appreciate love and just didn't throw it back into people's faces. Instead, I followed him back into the house.

"Now I have to take care of some telephone calls. But make yourself at home. The bar's over there."

Arnaz disappeared, and I walked over to the bar and fixed myself a drink. Through the big window, the brilliant blue California sky and the ocean.

Sitting in Desi Arnaz's living room, I remembered the episode of the *I Love Lucy* show in which my father and uncle had once appeared, except it now seemed to be playing itself out right before me. I blinked my eyes and my father and uncle were sitting on the couch opposite me. Then I heard the rattle of coffee cups and utensils and Lucille Ball walked into the living room. She then served the brothers their coffee.

When I thought, Poppy, my father looked up at me and smiled sadly.

"I'm so happy to see you again."

"And, son, I'm happy to see you."

My uncle smiled, too.

That's when Arnaz came in, but he wasn't the white-haired gentleman with the jowlish face and kind, weary eyes who had led me around the grounds. It was the cocky, handsome Arnaz of youth.

"Gee, fellows," he said. "It's nice to see you again. How are things down in Cuba?"

And I couldn't help myself. I walked over and sat on the couch and wrapped my arms around my father. Expected to find air, but hit on solid flesh. And his neck was warm. His expression pained and timid, like a hick off the boat. He was alive!

"Poppy, but I'm glad to see you."

"It is the same for me, son. It will always be the same."

Embracing him, I started to feel myself falling through an endless space, my father's heart. Not the heart of flesh and blood that had stopped beating, but this other heart filled with light and music, and I felt myself being pulled back into a world of pure affection, before torment, before loss, before awareness.

Spanish-English Glossary

ajo	garlic
arroz con pollo	rice with chicken
bolero	a slow Spanish dance
bueno	good
canción	song
chico	boy
compañero	partner, companion
cuídate	take care of yourself
Dios mío!	my God!
hombre	man
patrón	boss, patron
placita	place
plátanos (verde)	(green) plantains
¡Qué bueno!	How wonderful!
sí	yes
tranquilo	(stay) calm
tú sabes	you know
yuca	a root vegetable

MAP OF PLACES MENTIONED IN THE SELECTIONS

CONNECTICUT

New York City
NEW YORK

San Francisco
CALIFORNIA

Los Angeles
CALIFORNIA

Hollywood
CALIFORNIA

San Diego
CALIFORNIA

Havana CUBA

Oriente Province

Santiago de Cuba

PACIFIC OCEAN

Questions for the Reader

Thinking About the Story

1. What did you think about the selections from *The Mambo Kings Play Songs of Love*? What did you like and not like?

2. Did the events or people in the selections become important or special to you in some way? Write about or discuss these.

3. What do you think were the most important things Oscar Hijuelos wanted to say in the selections?

4. In what ways did the selections answer the questions you had before you began reading or listening?

5. Were any parts of the selections difficult to understand? If so, you may want to read or listen to them again. Discuss with your learning partners possible reasons why they were difficult.

Thinking About the Writing

1. How did Oscar Hijuelos help you see, hear and feel the atmosphere in the different scenes in the selections? Find the words, phrases or sentences that did this best.

2. Writers think carefully about their stories' settings, characters and events. In writing these selections, which of these things do you think Oscar Hijuelos felt was most important? Find the parts of the story that support your opinion.

3. In the selections, Oscar Hijuelos uses dialogue. Dialogue can make a story more alive. Pick out some dialogue that you feel is strong, and explain how it helps the story.

4. The selections from *The Mambo Kings Play Songs of Love* are written from different points of view. We hear the story of the *I Love Lucy* show from Eugenio's point of view years after his father and uncle were on the show and then we hear it as if it were really happening in the 1950s. What difference does the time and the point of view create in the writing of the selections?

5. Oscar Hijuelos, through his writing, makes us feel what it might have been like to be a Cuban-American musician in the 1950s. Find some parts in the selections that

helped you feel the mood of the time and the life of the characters.

Activities

1. Were there any words that were difficult for you in the selections from *The Mambo Kings Play Songs of Love*? Go back and try to figure out their meanings. Discuss what you think each word means and why you made that guess. Look them up in a dictionary and see if your definitions are the same or different.

   Discuss with your learning partners how you are going to remember each word. Some ways to remember words are to put them on file cards, write them in a journal or create a personal dictionary. Be sure to use the words in your writing.

2. Talking with other people about what you have read can increase your understanding of it. Discussion can help you organize your thoughts, get new ideas and rethink your original ideas. Discuss your thoughts about the selections from *The Mambo Kings Play Songs of Love* with someone else who has read them. Find out if your opinions are the same or different. See if your thoughts change as a result of this discussion.

3. After you finish reading or listening, you might want to write down your thoughts about the book. You could write a book review or a letter to a friend who might be interested in *The Mambo Kings Play Songs of Love*. You could write your reflections on the book in your journal, or you could write about topics the book has brought up that you want to explore further.

4. Did reading the selections give you any ideas for your own writing? You might want to write about:

   • a special moment that changed your life for better or for worse.

   • a story from your family's past.

   • how your favorite music makes you feel.

5. If you could talk to Oscar Hijuelos, what questions would you ask about his writing? You might want to write the questions in your journal.

6. Mambo music plays an important role in the lives of the Castillo brothers. Does your culture have a special dance or music? Do you have a favorite type of music or know certain dance steps? You might want to share what you know by playing recordings of the music or teaching the dance steps to others.

About Oscar Hijuelos

❉

Oscar Hijuelos was only a small child at the time of the mambo craze in New York. But he grew up hearing about New York in the 1950s from his relatives. These stories inspired him to write *The Mambo Kings Play Songs of Love*.

Hijuelos was born in New York in 1951. His parents were Cubans who left their native country for America. He grew up on Manhattan's Upper West Side, where he attended public high school. He spent a year at Bronx Community College and received his undergraduate degree from City College of New York. Today, the author still lives in his old neighborhood.

Hijuelos's first novel, *Our House in the Last World*, was published in 1983. Like *The Mambo Kings Play Songs of Love*, it is about the experience of Cuban-American immigrants.

Hijuelos has won many awards and fellowships. His most impressive honor was the Pulitzer Prize for Literature, one of the world's most important awards. He won it for *The Mambo Kings Play Songs of Love*.

To gather background information for the book, Hijuelos talked to many people about Latin music of the 1950s and the famous nightclubs of the time. In 1989, he told an interviewer from *The New York Times*: "The music, the dress, the language of nightclubs are all creativity and splendor. Dancing is pure creativity. It's an outlet."

His book was made into a movie, *The Mambo Kings*, starring Armand Assante and Antonio Banderas. Famous Latin musicians Tito Puente and Celia Cruz are also in the movie.

Latin Music and the Cuban-American Experience

Have you ever danced the mambo? If you went to nightclubs during the 1950s, you probably remember the mambo very well. At that time, the mambo was the most popular dance in the Western world. Today there is a second mambo craze, so you may have seen or danced the mambo.

The mambo is a lively but complicated dance that began in Cuba in the 1940s. As Cuban musicians came to America from Cuba at that time, the mambo became more and more popular. Bandleaders became famous not only in the Latin community but with all

Americans. Popular Latin dances included the mambo, rumba, cha-cha and merengue.

Cuba and Cuban-Americans

In the 1940s and 1950s, Havana, the capital of Cuba, was known for its glamorous night life. The city was full of nightclubs and casinos. Wealthy Americans went to Havana to enjoy the year-round warm weather as well as to gamble and enjoy the night life.

A number of performers in Havana night-clubs decided to move to the United States to perform for American audiences. Many of them came to New York City. In this way they helped to popularize the music and dances of Cuba, including the mambo. Cesar and Nestor Castillo, the main characters of *The Mambo Kings Play Songs of Love*, are modeled after Cuban musicians of that time.

In 1959, Fidel Castro, a Cuban revolutionary leader, took over the government of Cuba. He established a Communist government and closed the casinos and nightclubs. Many Cubans fled their native country for the United States. They settled in Miami, New York City and other big cities. Today there is a very large population of Cuban-Americans. Most of them came to this country ten years after the fictional characters of *The Mambo Kings Play Songs of Love*, however.

Desi Arnaz: A Cuban-American Success Story

One of the most famous and successful Cuban immigrants was Desi Arnaz. He was born in Cuba in 1917 and came to the United States as a young man. He began as a musician in Miami, then went to New York, eventually leading his own band.

Desi Arnaz starred in several plays and movies. One movie, *Too Many Girls*, which was filmed in 1940, also starred Lucille Ball. The two actors fell in love while making this movie and were married that year.

In 1950, Desi Arnaz and Lucille Ball decided to make a television series with themselves as stars. The networks didn't like the idea at first. They said that Desi Arnaz's accent was so heavy that audiences wouldn't accept him in the role of Lucille Ball's husband. But Lucy and Desi finally convinced CBS to produce the show. The weekly series ran from 1951 through 1957 and reruns are still shown today. It is among the most popular shows ever made.

Desi Arnaz and his wife were divorced in 1960. They had two children, Lucy Arnaz and Desi Arnaz, Jr. Desi Arnaz retired from acting but remained active in producing television shows. He died in 1986.

As you have seen in the selections from *The Mambo Kings Play Songs of Love*, Desi Arnaz was a hero to Cuban-Americans in the 1950s. No wonder Cesar and Nestor were so excited about their appearance on his show!

Doing the Mambo

The mambo is enjoying a new popularity among young people. Latin Americans and non–Latin Americans are dancing the mambo at nightclubs and even taking mambo lessons.

The mambo is often described as a faster version of the rumba. It is also related to the cha-cha. It is a very complicated yet exciting and even sexy dance step. It combines many influences from African, Spanish, Cuban and jazz music. Dancing the mambo requires a lot of skill and even more energy.

A Chronology
of Events
in the Selections

❊

1 Eugenio   Early 1960s

Eugenio sees his father and uncle on television when he is a boy in the early 1960s. This is a rerun of the *I Love Lucy* episode that originally ran in 1955. He watches with his Uncle Cesar. Page 13.

2 How it was   1955

Before this part of the selection begins, the Castillo brothers have left Cuba for New York City. They have started a band, the Mambo Kings, and are playing at nightclubs and dance halls around the country.

Desi Arnaz discovers the Mambo Kings at a New York nightclub in 1955. Page 22.

Desi Arnaz has a late dinner with the Castillo brothers. The star and his wife, Lucille Ball, return to the brothers' apartment, where Nestor's wife, Delores, cooks dinner. Pages 27–32.

The brothers fly to Hollywood to appear on I Love Lucy. Page 32–39. A description of this episode of the show begins on page 34.

The brothers become celebrities back in New York. Page 39.

3 Eugenio 1981

Eugenio Castillo visits Desi Arnaz in 1981. His father, Nestor, died in 1957. His uncle died in 1980 from alcoholism. Desi Arnaz is retired from show business and living in California. Page 40.